KT-503-770

Horrid
Henry's
Annual 2010

Horrid Henry's
Annual 2010

Francesca Simon

Illustrated by Tony Ross

Orion
Children's Books

First published in Great Britain in 2009
by Orion Children's Books
a division of the Orion Publishing Group Ltd
Orion House
5 Upper Saint Martin's Lane
London WC2H 9EA
An Hachette UK Company

1 3 5 7 9 8 6 4 2

This compilation, *Horrid Henry's Annual 2010* © Orion Children's Books 2009
TV animation images © Novel Entertainment Limited 2009
Designed by EnvyDesignLtd
Illustrations © Tony Ross 2009
Compiled by Sally Byford from the *Horrid Henry* books
by Francesca Simon & illustrated by Tony Ross

All rights reserved. No part of this publication may be
reproduced, stored in a retrieval system, or transmitted, in
any form or by any means, electronic, mechanical,
photocopying, recording or otherwise, without the prior
permission of Orion Children's Books

The Orion Publishing Group's policy is to use papers that are natural, renewable and recyclable
products and made from wood grown in sustainable forests. The logging and manufacturing processes
are expected to conform to the environmental regulations of the country of origin.

ISBN 978 1 84255 720 4

A catalogue record for this book is available from the British Library

Printed and bound in Italy by Rotolito Lombarda

www.orionbooks.co.uk
www.horridhenry.co.uk

Contents

Hello Everyone,

Welcome to my brilliant 2010 annual. This year is going to be the best ever. I'll show Moody Margaret who's boss once and for all. Everyone will follow the special New Year's resolutions I wrote for them, I'll get to go on my ideal holiday, and for once I'll get EVERYTHING I ask for at Christmas. Nah nah ne nah nah.

Henry

Find the Filthy Fingerprints
Horrid Henry has flicked through the Annual and left lots of filthy fingerprints. Can you count how many there are?

Horrid Henry versus Moody Margaret

Horrid Henry and Moody Margaret are sworn enemies, but if you put them head to head, who would come out on top?

	Henry	Margaret
1. When Nurse Needle comes to school to give everyone injections, one person is brave and the other is a big cry-baby coward. Who's the brave one?		
2. Who is the best footballer in the class?		
3. When Nitty Nora checks everyone's heads, she says: "No nits. Keep up the good work" to one person. Who is it?		
4. Who gets the bigger part in the school Christmas play?		
5. When Horrid Henry and Moody Margaret make Glop, one of them wriggles out of eating any. Who is it?		
6. When the class has a swimming test, only one person gets a badge. Who is it?		

When Margaret comes to stay at Henry's house, it's Henry's worst nightmare, especially when she takes over his bedroom…

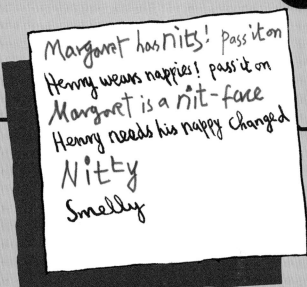

Margaret has nits! Pass it on
Henry wears nappies! pass it on
Margaret is a nit-face
Henry needs his nappy changed
Nitty
Smelly

Horrid Henry sat listening by the door. He'd scattered crumbs all over Margaret's bed. He couldn't wait to hear her scream.

But there wasn't a sound coming from Henry's room, where Margaret the invader lay. Henry couldn't understand it.

Sadly, he climbed into (oh, the shame of it) the bottom bunk.

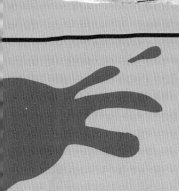

Then he screamed. His bed was filled with jam, crumbs, and something squishy squashy and horrible.

"Go to sleep, Henry!" shouted Dad.

That Margaret! He'd booby-trap the room, cut up her doll's clothes, paint her face purple… Henry smiled grimly.

Oh yes, he'd fix Moody Margaret.

Find out how Henry really does fix Moody Margaret in 'Moody Margaret Moves In' from **Horrid Henry Tricks the Tooth Fairy.**

Crazy Cartoons

Have a go at creating your own simple cartoon.

You will need:

A small notebook or about twenty pieces of paper stapled together at one edge to create your own notebook
Pencils, pens or crayons
Rubber

Instructions:

1. Decide what you want to draw in your cartoon, and what you would like to happen. It's best to try something simple first, like the bouncing ball example shown over the page.
2. When you flick through your cartoon, do it from the back of the notebook to the start. Draw your first picture on the last page of the notebook.
3. When you're happy with your first picture, go through the notebook drawing the same picture, but change it slightly each time.
4. When you've finished, flick through the notebook from back to front, and your picture should look like it's moving.
5. Use felt-tip pens to add colour, or go over your pencil line in black.

BOUNCING BALL

Try a bouncing ball. Here's an example using fifteen pages.

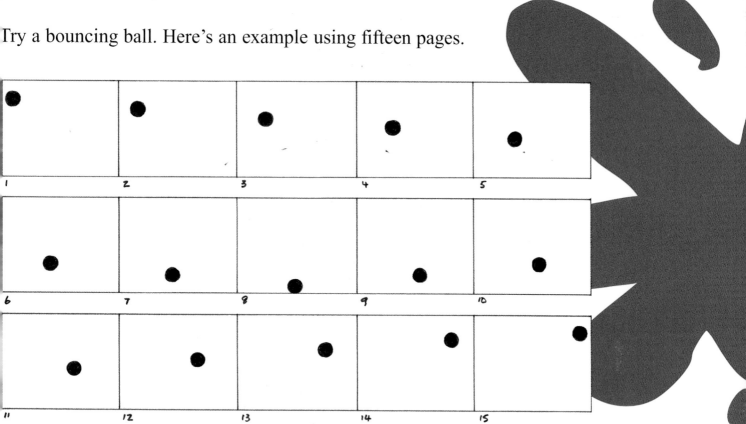

MAKE HORRID HENRY SMILE

If you want to do a smiling face – like Horrid Henry below – copy the same picture for each of the images, but change the mouth from frowning to smiling.

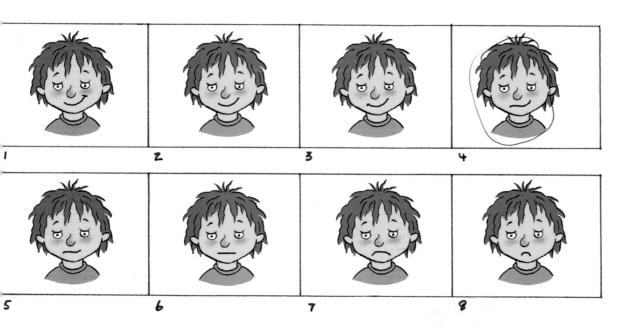

Horrid Henry's 2010 Book Challenge

When Miss Battle-Axe announces to the class that she is holding a reading competition, Henry is determined to win.

Horrid Henry smiled. Wouldn't they get a shock when he won the prize? He'd start reading the second he got home. He'd start reading the second he got home.

Horrid Henry stretched out in the comfy black chair and switched on the TV. He had plenty of time to read. He'd start tomorrow.

Find out if Henry does win the prize in **'Horrid Henry Reads a Book'** from **Horrid Henry's Stinkbomb**.

HENRY'S LIST

The Happy Nappy
Mouse Goes to Town
Mouse Goes to the Country
Mouse Goes Round the World
Mouse Goes to the Loo
A Boy and his Pig
A Pig and his Boy
A Boyish Pig
A Piggish Boy
Two Pigs and a Boy
The Boys and a Pig

Keep a list of the first ten books you read this year. You could give them a score out of five stars too.

☆ stinky   ☆☆ OK   ☆☆☆ good   ☆☆☆☆ very good   ☆☆☆☆☆ brilliant

MY LIST OF BOOKS

	Title	Author	Stars ☆☆☆☆☆
1			
2			
3			
4			
5			
6			
7			
8			
9			
10			

What's the best Horrid Henry book ever?

Tell us your Top Favourite Five-Star Most Brilliant Horrid Henry book by emailing to myfavourites@orionbooks.co.uk and we'll list the top three in the next Horrid Henry Annual.

HENRY'S HOWLERS

What has a spine but no bones?

A book.

Horrid Henry's New Year's Resolutions (for other people)

Of course, I don't need to write New Year's resolutions, because I'm perfect already. But certain other people need all the help they can get…

MUM'S NEW YEAR'S RESOLUTIONS

- Let Henry eat all the sweets he wants – especially Chocolate Hairballs and Belcher Squelchers
- Let Henry watch as much TV as he wants, and always let him sit in the comfy black chair and control the remote
- Never tell Henry off
- Give Henry £1000 pocket money a week
- Buy Henry a present every day
- Buy Henry three huge TVs for his bedroom

DAD'S NEW YEAR'S RESOLUTIONS
- Only put sweets and crisps and fizzywhizz drinks in Henry's packed lunch box
- Never make Henry eat vegetables
- Make Peter do all of Henry's chores
- Remember that everything is always Peter's fault
- Henry is the boss: whatever he says goes
- Put Peter in the bin where he belongs

PETER'S NEW YEAR'S RESOLUTIONS
- Give Henry all my money
- Give Henry all my chips
- Always walk three paces behind Henry, and never ever sit in the comfy black chair
- Always call Henry 'Lord High Majesty of the Purple Hand'
- Always let Henry sit on the right hand side of the car behind the driver
- Always let Henry have first dibs on the Sweet Tweets cereal boxes so he can get the prize inside
- Remember that I am a lowly wormy worm and not fit to breath the same air as Henry

MISS BATTLE-AXE'S NEW YEAR'S RESOLUTIONS
- No homework ever for Henry
- Henry to be given the lead in the school play
- Henry to be given straight As and perfect reports
- Henry to be excused from all tests

Criss-Cross Conqueror

Henry aimed the hoover at Margaret. He was a fire-breathing dragon burning his prey to a crisp.

Find out what happens when Moody Margaret comes to stay in '**Moody Margaret Moves In**' from *Horrid Henry Tricks the Tooth Fairy.*

When Horrid Henry attacks Moody Margaret or Perfect Peter, he's not a boy any more, he's a dragon or a shark or an alien. Find some of his wildest daydreams below.

4 letters
CRAB
BULL

5 letters
SHARK
ALIEN

6 letters
PIRATE
DRAGON

7 letters
WARRIOR
MONSTER
OCTOPUS
VAMPIRE

8 letters
ELEPHANT

9 letters
CROCODILE

Start with the longest words.

Clever Clare's Cross Cress Egg Head

Clever Clare has created a very cross cress egg head – it's Moody Margaret with her wacky sticking-up hairdo!

Try making your own egg head.

You will need:

Egg
Cotton wool or kitchen towel
Felt tip pens
Cress seeds

Instructions:

1. To prepare your egg, carefully crack the top off a raw egg, so you're left with as much of the eggshell as possible. Then rinse out your eggshell so it's clean inside.
2. Stand your eggshell in an egg cup or empty egg box, and draw a face on one side of the egg. Be creative!
3. Fill half the egg with cotton wool or kitchen paper, and dampen with warm water.
4. Sprinkle some cress seeds onto the cotton wool or paper and put your egg somewhere dark until the first shoots start to appear.
5. Then move to a sunny spot and watch your egghead's hair begin to grow.

21

Which Character is Which?

Use the clues to guess the characters below!

1.

This belongs to me...

I wear these...

I said: "It's my club and I decide."

My fascinating food fact is: I won't eat my supper if the vegetables are touching the meat on my plate.

Who am I? _____

2.

This belongs to me...

I wear these...

I said: "I don't want to improve my spelling! ... I want to play games."

My fascinating food fact is: I like eating snails! _____

Who am I? _____

3.

This belongs to me…

I wear these…

I said: "I've written all my thank you letters."

My fascinating food fact is: I love all vegetables, except for beetroot.

Who am I? _____

4.

This belongs to me…

I wear this…

I said (about my best friend!): "On the ugly scale of I to 10, with I being the ugliest, wartiest toad, you're a 2."

My fascinating food fact is: I like eating cakes, but they don't make me sweet.

Who am I? _____

5.

These belong to me…

I wear these…

I said: "I'm watching you, Henry."

My fascinating food fact is: My mum says I chew with my mouth open.

Who am I? _____

Horrid Henry's Guide to Getting Out of Homework

"Henry! Why aren't you doing your homework?" said Dad.

"I'm tired!" yawned Henry. "I'm just taking a little break. It's hard having so much work!"

"Henry, you've only got five words to learn!" said Dad. "And you've just spent two hours *not* learning them."

"All right," snarled Henry. Slowly, he picked up his spelling list. Then he put it down again. He had to get in the mood. Soothing music, that's what he needed. Horrid Henry switched on his cassette player. The terrible sound of the Driller Cannibals boomed through the house.

"OH, I'm a CAN-CAN-CANNIBAL!" screamed Henry, stomping around his room. "DON'T CALL ME AN ANIMAL JUST 'CAUSE I'M A CAN-CAN-CANNIBAL!"

Does Henry ever do his homework? Find out in **'Horrid Henry's Homework'** from **Horrid Henry and the Mummy's Curse.**

How I avoid getting any homework

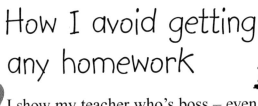

- I show my teacher who's boss – even if it's Mr Nerdon, the toughest, meanest teacher in the school. If I make my teacher run screaming from the classroom, then they can't give me any homework to do.

- Before Miss Battle-Axe can say 'homework', I get a tummy ache double quick so I have to be sent home. If that doesn't work, I run out of the door screaming I've got mad cow disease. That works every time.

- If the homework is learning stupid, boring, useless spellings, I explain to Miss Battle-Axe that I don't need to learn to spell because I never write letters, and never will. This hasn't worked yet – but I keep trying!

How I get out of doing my homework

I promise Mum and Dad I'll do my homework after my favourite TV show, Knight Fight. By that time, they've forgotten all about it – tee hee!

I go green and hide my homework sheets in the recycling box. Mum and Dad can't tell me off because I'm doing my best to save the planet.

I pretend that I've learned my spellings – then make sure I'm sitting next to Clever Clare or Brainy Brian so I can copy all their work.

Excuses I've given Miss Battle-Axe

Our hamster, Fang, chewed up my homework.

Peter spilled his drink all over my homework.

We had a surprise visit from Great-Aunt Greta last night, and I wanted to spend all my time with her.

I wrote my essay in invisible ink, and it won't appear.

"But, Miss Battle-Axe, you only said we had to write an essay about our weekend. You didn't say we had to bring it in." (This only worked once!)

An alien spaceship landed in our garden, and the aliens stole my homework.

Our house burned down – and all my homework with it.

Spot the Difference

"Margaret is coming to stay while her parents go on holiday," said Mum.

Henry was speechless with horror.

"She's going to stay … here?"

"Yes," said Mum.

"How long?" said Henry.

"Two weeks," said Mum brightly.

Horrid Henry could not stand Moody Margaret for more than two minutes.

Find how Horrid Henry copes with his unwanted guest in 'Moody Margaret Moves In' from **Horrid Henry Tricks the Tooth Fairy**.

Margaret stays in Henry's room, and she scatters her toys all over it. Spot the difference between these two pictures and find Margaret's ten hidden toys.

Write down the ten toys here:

April Fools' Day Tricks

Henry thinks April Fools' Day is the perfect time for tricking Margaret and her Secret Club gang. Here are some of the tricks he's planning to play this year:

I'm going to sneak into the Secret Club den! First I'll raid their biscuit tin, fill it with soil and hide a worm or two in there. Just wait until they get hungry!

Then I'll squeeze some lemon juice into their bottles of water. When they have a drink, it'll taste really nasty and sour — just like Susan!

But Margaret likes April Fools' Day too, and she's determined to get her own back on the boys.

I'll superglue the tops onto the Secret Club water bottles, then say very sweetly to Henry or Ralph or one of the other stinky boys, "You look really strong. Please could you take the top off this bottle for me." Ha ha — then they'll look really stupid!

Horrid Henry's Horrid Holidays

Ahh! Holidays! Sitting on a sofa, eating crisps, watching telly, scoffing ten huge burgers and chips every night at Gobble and Go... Maybe this year Mum and Dad will give me the holiday I want rather than the one they want. They like ... museums. Nature. Sightseeing. Reading. What kind of a holiday is *that*??

Here are my top suggestions for horrid holidays for evil enemies ... tee hee.

For Stuck-Up Steve:
Swimming in a shark-infested
swimming pool

For Bossy Bill:
Camping in a jungle swamp filled
with poisonous man-eating snakes

For Moody Margaret:
Homework Camp

For Perfect Peter:
Goo-Shooter World

For Rabid Rebecca:
Spider Camp

For Miss Battle-Axe:
Bungee jumping

Summer Holiday Wordsearch

Henry overhears the girls boasting about the exciting places they're visiting this summer. Moody Margaret is going to Majorca, Clever Clare to Corfu and Magic Martha to Miami. Find all the girls' holiday destinations in the wordsearch.

BALI

ORLANDO

MIAMI

BARBADOS

CRETE

CORFU

EGYPT

FLORIDA

MAJORCA

M	M	B	E	U	V	O	S
I	K	A	J	G	D	U	O
A	M	L	J	N	L	F	D
M	J	I	A	O	I	R	A
I	P	L	R	I	R	O	B
R	R	E	T	E	R	C	R
O	F	L	O	R	I	D	A
E	G	Y	P	T	Y	L	B

Perfect Peter's Pencil and Paper Page

Perfect Peter loves sprouts, and he even knows a game for two players called Spotty Sprouts. It's good fun to play on long car journeys.

Spotty Sprouts

1. Before you start, draw four or five dots on a piece of paper.

2. Take it in turns to draw a line connecting two of the dots. Your line can be as wiggly as you like.

You can connect any two of the dots, as long as you follow these two rules:

Rule One – none of the dots can have more than three lines coming from it.

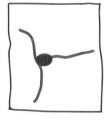

Rule Two – you can't draw across any of the lines.

3. Each time you draw a line connecting two dots, draw a new dot in the middle of the line.

4. The winner is the last person who can draw a line without breaking any of the rules. The game below started with two dots, the green player started and has won the game.

31

Little Brother and Sister Taming Tips

Horrid Henry believes that all little brothers and sisters need taming – especially Perfect Peter

In the last Annual, Henry asked readers to send in their own ideas for taming little brother. and sisters. Below are some of his favourite ones. Henry's planning to try all of them out on Peter – when Mum and Dad aren't looking!

Never let your little brother or sister forget that you are the best, the mightiest and the toughest ... and that you rule!

When your little brother or sister decides to make your mum and dad breakfast in bed, offer to carry it upstairs for them because it looks too heavy. Mum and Dad will think you've made it and give you extra pocket money!

Make your little brother do chores like bring you crisps in a bowl, be your servant for ninety years and treat you like the king or queen.

Tell your little brother that you'll take him to cinema, but he has to practise being quiet first ... then don't take him!

Pretend to be nice to your brother and play Hide and Seek. But when it's your turn to seek, leave him in his hiding place and go to play in your room.

I can't wait to try these out – tee hee!

Join the Club

Which club should you join – the Purple Hand, the Secret Club or the Best Boys' Club? Follow the flow chart to find out!

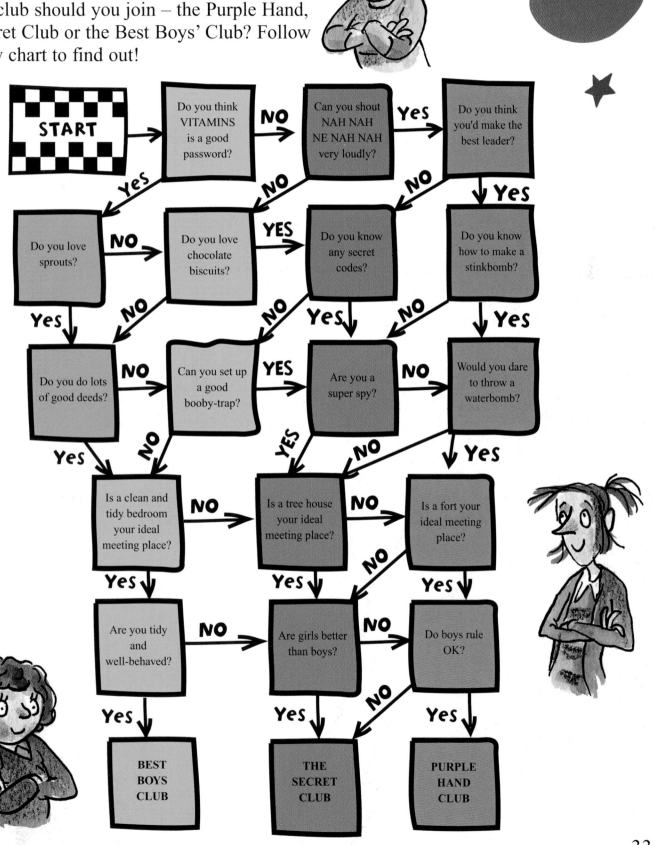

START

Do you think VITAMINS is a good password? — **NO** → Can you shout NAH NAH NE NAH NAH very loudly? — **Yes** → Do you think you'd make the best leader?

Do you love sprouts? — **NO** → Do you love chocolate biscuits? — **YES** → Do you know any secret codes? — **NO** → Do you know how to make a stinkbomb?

Do you do lots of good deeds? — **NO** → Can you set up a good booby-trap? — **YES** → Are you a super spy? — **NO** → Would you dare to throw a waterbomb?

Is a clean and tidy bedroom your ideal meeting place? — **NO** → Is a tree house your ideal meeting place? — **NO** → Is a fort your ideal meeting place?

Are you tidy and well-behaved? — **NO** → Are girls better than boys? — **NO** → Do boys rule OK?

BEST BOYS CLUB

THE SECRET CLUB

PURPLE HAND CLUB

Horrid Henry's Hobbies

Everyone know what Horrid Henry loves doing best!

Ah, Saturday! Best day of the week, thought Horrid Henry, flinging off the covers and leaping out of bed. No school! No homework! A day of TV heaven! Mum and Dad liked sleeping in on a Saturday. So long as Henry and Peter were quiet they could watch TV until Mum and Dad woke up.

Horrid Henry could picture it now. He would stretch out in the comfy black chair, grab the remote control, and switch on the TV. All his favourite shows were on today: *Rapper Zapper*, *Mutant Max*, and *Gross-Out*.

Does Henry's weekend go as planned? Find out in **'Horrid Henry and the Comfy Black Chair'** from **Horrid Henry's Haunted House**.

But Henry does have other hobbies, apart from watching TV. He even shares an interest with Perfect Peter – and it isn't stamp collecting or playing the cello…

Horrid Henry and Perfect Peter both collected Gizmos from inside Sweet Tweet cereal boxes. So did everyone at their school. There were ten different coloured Gizmos to collect, from the common green to the rare gold. Both Henry and Peter had Gizmos of every colour. Except for one. Gold.

Read **'Horrid Henry's Hobby'** from **Horrid Henry and the Mummy's Curse** and find out if Henry ever gets a gold Gizmo.

Two of Henry's classmates take their hobbies very seriously, like Aerobic Al…

Flash! A small figure wearing gleaming white trainers zipped by. It was Aerobic Al, the fastest boy in Henry's class.

"Gotta run, gotta run, gotta run," he chanted, gliding into place beside Henry. "I will, of course, win every event," he announced. "I've been training all year. My dad's got a special place all ready for my trophies."

Does Aerobic Al win all the races? You can find out in **'Horrid Henry's Sports Day'** from *Horrid Henry Gets Rich Quick*.

…and Moody Margaret…

Margaret marched down the hall, playing her trumpet.
TOOT A TOOT, TOOT A TOOT, TOOT A TOOT TOOT TOOT TOOT.

"Margaret, would you mind playing your trumpet a little later?" said Dad, clutching his ears. "It's six o'clock in the morning."

"That's when I wake up," said Margaret.

"Could you play a little more softly?" said Mum.

"But I have to practise," said Moody Margaret, The trumpet blared through the house.
TOOT TOOT TOOT.

Read the full story in **'Moody Margaret Moves In'** from *Horrid Henry Tricks the Tooth Fairy*.

Greedy Graham's Grub

Greedy Graham loves summer picnics, with lots of delicious treats to eat. Try his scrumptious sandwich idea.

TRIPLE DECKER SANDWICH

You will need:

Three slices of bread, brown or white
Butter or margarine
Any fillings of your choice – like chicken, ham, tuna, cheese, tomatoes, cucumber, lettuce, bacon, peanut butter

Instructions:

1. Butter two of the slices of bread on one side.
2. Choose your sandwich filling, and put it between the two slices of bread.
3. Now butter the top of the sandwich, and one side of the third slice of bread.
4. Choose a different sandwich filling, pile it on top of your original sandwich, and put the third slice of bread on the top of that.
5. If you want to make a tall skyscraper sandwich to share, you can carry on building more sandwich layers – but don't forget, the taller your sandwich, the harder it will be to eat!

GREEDY GRAHAM'S TOP TIP

Make sure all your fillings taste nice together – otherwise you'll have a triple-decker disaster!

Sandwich Criss-Cross

Find all these favourite sandwich fillings hidden in the wordsearch.

Start with the longest words.

3 Letters
EGG
HAM

4 LETTERS
TUNA
BEEF
PATÉ

5 LETTERS
HONEY
SALAD
BACON
CHIPS

6 LETTERS
CHEESE
TOMATO
SALAMI

7 LETTERS
CHICKEN

What's your favourite filling?

I like healthy egg sandwiches.

Honey's sweet like me.

I dunno.

Chips!

Horrid Henry Outwits his Friends and Enemies

Horrid Henry loves getting the better of his friends and enemies. He's always thinking up ways to outwit them.

It's Sports Day and Horrid Henry hasn't got a hope of winning, unless he comes up with a clever plan…

Henry heaved his heavy bones to the starting line. His final chance to win... yet he knew there was no hope. If he beat Weepy William he'd be doing well.

Suddenly Henry had a wonderful, spectacular idea. Why had he never thought of this before? Truly, he was a genius. Wasn't there some ancient Greek who'd won a race by throwing down golden apples which his rival kept stopping to pick up? Couldn't he, Henry, learn something from those old Greeks.

"Ready… steady…GO!" shrieked Miss Battle-Axe.

Off they dashed.

"Go, Al, go!" yelled his father.

"Get a move on, Margaret!" shrieked her mother.

"Go, Ralph!" cheered his father.

"Do your best, Henry," said Mum.

Horrid Henry reached into his pocket and hurled some sweets. They thudded to the ground in front of the runners.

Read the full story and find out if Henry's plan works in **'Horrid Henry's Sports Day'** from **Horrid Henry Gets Rich Quick**.

When Horrid Henry goes to work with his dad, he meets his match in Bossy Bill.
Henry has to think fast...

Scowling, Horrid Henry followed Bill into the photocopy room.

"Ha ha ha ha ha, I got you into trouble!" chortled Bill.

Horrid Henry resisted the urge to mash Bossy Bill into tiny bite-sized chunks. Instead, Horrid Henry started to think. Even if he was good as gold all day it would mean Bill had won. He had to come up with a plan to get back at Bill. Fast. But what? Anything awful Bill did Henry was sure to get the blame. No one would believe Henry hadn't done it. If his plan to work, Bill had to be caught red-handed.

And then Horrid Henry had it. A perfectly brilliant, spectacularly evil plan. A plan to end all plans. A plan to go down in history. A plan – but there was no time to lose congratulating himself.

What is Henry's master plan? Does it work? Find out in **'Horrid Henry Goes to Work'** from **Horrid Henry's Revenge**.

Horrid Henry is always trying to outwit Moody Margaret. When he turns his hand to hypnotism, Henry wastes no time in getting Margaret to obey his orders…

…But first, what should he make Margaret do?

Ah, yes. Her house was filled with sweets and biscuits and fizzy drinks – all the things Henry's horrible parents never let him have.

"Bring us all your sweets, all your biscuits and a Fizzywizz drink."

"Yes, master," said Moody Margaret.

Henry stretched out in the hammock. So did Rude Ralph. This was the life!

Can Henry outwit Margaret – or will she get the better of him in the end?
Find out in **'Moody Margaret Casts a Spell'** in **Horrid Henry Meets the Queen**.

What do you think is the best way of outwitting an enemy?

_____

_____

Club Know-How Quiz

How much do you know about Horrid Henry's Purple Hand Club, Moody Margaret's Secret Club and Perfect Peter's Best Boys' Club?

1. **Which club is Tidy Ted is in?**
   (a) The Purple Hand
   (b) The Secret Club
   (c) The Best Boys

2. **What is Perfect Peter's title in the Secret Club?**
   (a) Deputy
   (b) Worm
   (c) Junior

3. **Which club votes to ban boys?**
   (a) The Purple Hand
   (b) The Secret Club
   (c) The Best Boys

4. **Who is the Deputy Leader of the Purple Hand Club?**
   (a) Rude Ralph
   (b) Beefy Bert
   (c) Greedy Graham

5. **Who is the Deputy Leader of the Secret Club?**
   (a) Sour Susan
   (b) Lazy Linda
   (c) Whoever is Margaret's best friend at the time!

6. Which club has the password 'Nunga'?
- (a) The Purple Hand
- (b) The Secret Club
- (c) The Best Boys

7. What title has Horrid Henry bestowed upon himself?
- (a) Lord High Excellent Majesty
- (b) Lord High Leader
- (c) Big Boss Purple Hand

8. Which club keeps their biscuits in a skull and crossbones biscuit tin?
- (a) The Purple Hand
- (b) The Secret Club
- (c) The Best Boys

How did you do? You'll find the answers on page 74.

1 – 3
You must be the club clown! Perfect Peter might let you in the Best Boys' Club as his good deed for the day, but you've got no chance of joining the Purple Hand or the Secret Club.

4 – 6
You're not a club leader yet, but Horrid Henry might let you spy for the Purple Hand, and Moody Margaret might let you spy for the Secret Club. If you're sneaky, you could be a double agent!

7 – 8
Congratulations! You're completely clued-up about the clubs. But don't bother begging to join the Purple Hand or the Secret Club – start your own rival club instead!

Henry's Secret Code

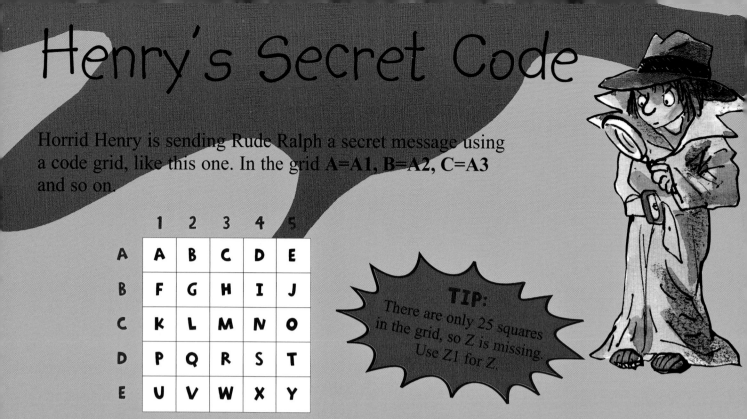

Horrid Henry is sending Rude Ralph a secret message using a code grid, like this one. In the grid **A=A1, B=A2, C=A3** and so on.

	1	2	3	4	5
A	A	B	C	D	E
B	F	G	H	I	J
C	K	L	M	N	O
D	P	Q	R	S	T
E	U	V	W	X	Y

TIP:
There are only 25 squares in the grid, so Z is missing. Use Z1 for Z.

BUT Moody Margaret already knows *this* code, so Henry sneakily mixes up the letters of the alphabet. He puts his name first, then the alphabet. Now Margaret can't read his secret message – unless she steals the grid!

	1	2	3	4	5
A	H	E	N	R	Y
B	A	B	C	D	F
C	G	I	J	K	L
D	M	O	P	Q	S
E	T	U	V	W	X

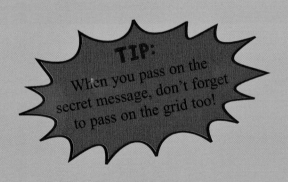

TIP:
When you pass on the secret message, don't forget to pass on the grid too!

Here is Henry's message. Can you uncode it?
D5/E1/C2/A3/C4/A5   B5/C2/D5/A1

Write your answer here:

MOODY MARGARET IS A

_ _ _ _ _ _ _   _ _ _ _ _

Secret Club Code Circle

Disaster! Moody Margaret has cracked the code! She's so angry she sends him a message back. She tells Henry to start at the letter **H**, and go round the circle twice, writing down every other letter until he's discovered the message. Have a go yourself!

START

Answer:

_ _ _ _ _ _ _ _ _ _ _ _ _

_ _ _ _ _ _ _ _ _ _ _ _ _

Hello From Around the World

Look in the wordsearch to find out how Henry says hello from countries around the world.

KALIMERA (Greece)

BONJOUR (France)

HOLA (Spain)

MERHABA (Turkey)

NAZDAR (Czechoslovakia)

ALOHA (Hawaii)

SZIA (Hungary)

HALLO (Netherlands)

A	Y	A	I	Z	S	S	R
H	R	X	L	D	N	A	U
A	S	E	X	O	B	G	O
L	S	Q	M	A	H	H	J
L	Z	Q	H	I	O	A	N
O	D	R	A	L	L	X	O
Y	E	L	A	R	N	A	B
M	N	A	Z	D	A	R	K

Bonjour! I'm Lucas La Cata from France

Kalimera! I'm Anipoforos Christoforos from Greece

Hallo! I'm Stoute Hendrik from the Netherlands

Hola! I'm Pablo Diablo from Spain

Horrid Henry Goes to Play

Horrid Henry sets off to spend the day at Rude Ralph's house. But can he find his way through the maze of streets or will he end up at Sour Susan's house instead?

Horrid Henry's House

Rude Ralph's House

Sour Susan's House

Horrid Henry Goes Back to School

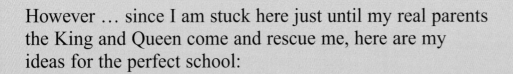

Oh yuck! What am i doing here when I could be comfy at home watching TV? When I grow up I'm going to be King Henry the Horrible so I don't need to learn to read and multiply and spell. I will have a royal reader to read all my royal decrees, and a royal multiplier who will count my gold and treasure and a royal speller who will write all my no-thank you letters, so really I don't need to be in school at all.

However … since I am stuck here just until my real parents the King and Queen come and rescue me, here are my ideas for the perfect school:

Everyone must bring their goo-shooters to school every day

Halls are for skateboarding

School starts at lunchtime, ends after playtime

No homework, ever

Teachers have to do P.E.

Gobble and Go will run the school cafeteria

Miss Battle-Axe to return to the salt mines where she belongs

Henry to be Head!!

Back to School Clock Puzzle

It's the first day back at school. When Henry's alarm goes off, he stays in bed and daydreams. Follow the time instructions and write the letters in the answer spaces below to find out what Henry's dream is all about.

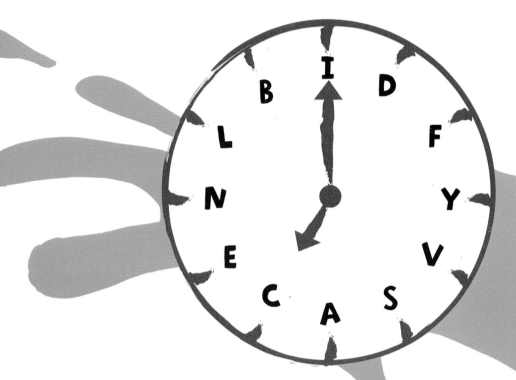

WHERE DOES THE BIG HAND GO WHEN IT'S...

1. Seven o'clock
2. Quarter to seven
3. Twenty past seven
4. Half past seven
5. Five past seven
6. Twenty to seven
7. Five past seven
8. Five to seven

9. Quarter past seven
10. Half past seven
11. Ten to seven
12. Seven o'clock
13. Twenty to seven
14. Quarter to seven
15. Twenty-five past seven

HENRY DREAMS THAT HIS SCHOOL HAS BEEN

_ _ _ _ _   _ _   _ _ _ _ _ _

Whose Handwriting?

Did you know that you can tell what a person is like from their handwriting?
You just have to follow a few simple rules:

Rule 1: Upright or sloping

hello   If your writing is upright like this you're nice and sensible.

hello   If your writing slopes to the left, you're shy and secretive, and can be moody.

hello   If your writing slopes to the right, you're friendly and talkative and sometimes very noisy.

Rule 2: Large or small

Loud, confident people have big, bold writing like this: boo!

Quiet, clever people have small, dainty writing like this: boo!

Rule 3: Neat or messy

goodbye   Neat writers like to be in charge.

goodbye   Messy writers are lazy and scruffy.

Dear Margaret
I HATE you.
I hope you marry
a toad

Henry

What's Horrid Henry's handwriting like?

- It slopes to the right
- It's large and bold
- It's messy

Horrid Henry's writing shows he is:

- Friendly, talkative and noisy
- Loud and confident
- Lazy and scruffy

You can tell from this handwriting that I'm very clever and very brilliant.

What's Moody Margaret's handwriting like?

- It slopes to the left
- It's small and dainty
- It's neat

A toad would rather get squished in the road than marry you, So ha ha ha. Margaret.

This writing is obviously by the moodiest, meanest girl in the whole world.

Moody Margaret's handwriting shows that she is:

- Shy and secretive, and can be moody
- Quiet and clever
- Likes to be in charge

What are you like?

Write a short sentence below, and see what the handwriting rules reveal?

Rude Ralph's Slimy Slime

Rude Ralph has a really revolting recipe to make some green slimy slime. It's just the stuff for April Fools' Day – or any other day!

You will need:

Water
Measuring jug
Pan
Green food colouring
Unflavoured gelatine
(3 envelopes)
Golden syrup
Fork

Instructions:

1. Measure 2 fl oz of water, pour it into the pan and heat until it boils.

2. Take the pan off the heat. Add a tiny drop of green food colouring to the water.

3. Sprinkle in three envelopes of gelatine.

4. Leave the gelatine to soften for 2-3 minutes, then stir with a fork.

5. Add two dessertspoons of golden syrup.

6. Stir with a fork and lift out the long slimy strands of green goo.

7. As it cools, you'll need to add more water, a little at a time.

RUDE RALPH'S TIP:

When the slime is cool, it's time to play tricks!
Sneak some slime into a tissue, give a big sneeze, then reveal the green gunk inside the tissue!

Find the Halloween Pairs

Horrid Henry sets out to scare on Halloween night!
Can you find the four matching pairs?

A

B

C

D

E

F

G

H

THE FOUR MATCHING PAIRS ARE:

_____ and _____   _____ and _____

_____ and _____   _____ and _____

51

Make a Scary Mask

Here's how to make a mask like Horrid Henry's pointy-nosed mask below. Or you could be even scarier – and make a Miss Battle-Axe mask!

You will need:

Cardboard or thick paper – black for the eye mask, or white for Miss Battle-Axe's spectacles

Scissors

Pencils, felt tip pens or paints

Sticky tape

PVA glue

Length of elastic

> My mask looks brilliant if you make it out of black cardboard or paper.

Instructions:

1. On cardboard or thick paper, draw the mask you're making using the guide over page. Also draw the nose of the mask.

2. Cut out eye holes.

3. Strengthen the sides of the masks with sticky tape. Cut a small hole on either side, where shown, to thread the elastic through.

4. Now thread the elastic on one side, so that the end is at the back of the mask. Tie a knot, and secure with sticky tape. Cut the correct length of elastic, leaving about 3cm to tie another knot. Again, thread through on the other side, tie a knot and secure with sticky tape.

5. Make folds in the nose where shown, and tape or glue to the mask.

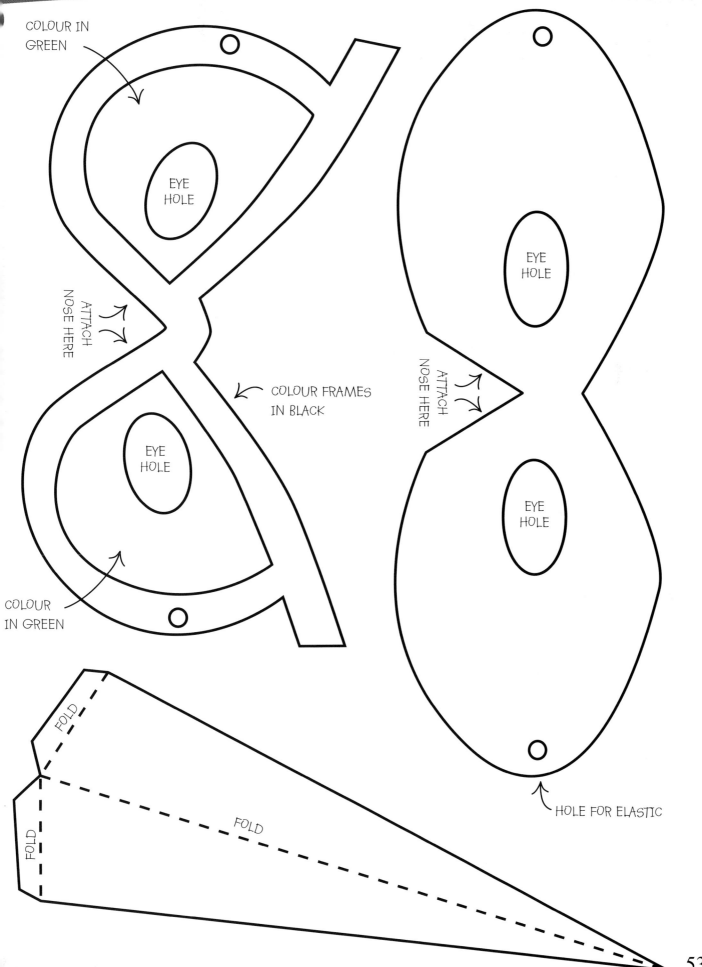

COLOUR IN
GREEN

EYE
HOLE

ATTACH
NOSE HERE

COLOUR FRAMES
IN BLACK

EYE
HOLE

COLOUR
IN GREEN

EYE
HOLE

ATTACH
NOSE HERE

EYE
HOLE

EYE
HOLE

HOLE FOR ELASTIC

FOLD

FOLD

FOLD

53

Anxious Andrew's Worried Wordsearch

Anxious Andrew doesn't like Halloween –
it's far too worrying! Find all the things that
make Andrew anxious on Halloween in
the wordsearch.

S	W	I	T	C	H	E	S
N	S	V	T	O	Y	R	P
I	K	E	F	X	E	M	O
K	S	F	N	D	J	S	O
P	A	U	I	K	T	A	K
M	M	P	G	A	R	J	S
U	S	M	B	Z	N	A	N
P	S	T	S	O	H	G	D

SPIDERS   **DARKNESS**
SPOOKS   **MASKS**
WITCHES   **BATS**
GHOSTS   **PUMPKINS**

HENRY'S HOWLERS

What do canaries do on
Halloween night?

They go trick or tweeting.

54

Mad Misfits

Look at these crazy mixed-up characters! You'll recognise their faces, but can you guess who the other two bits of body belong to?

You'll find the following characters:

Sour Susan and **Miss Battle-Axe** (they both appear twice), **Brainy Brian**, **Henry's dad**, **Gorgeous Gurinder**, **Greedy Graham**, **Moody Margaret**, **Perfect Peter**, **Soggy Sid** and **Weepy William**.

FIGURE 1

1 ———————

2 ———————

3 ———————

FIGURE 2

1 ———————

2 ———————

3 ———————

FIGURE 3

1 ———————

2 ———————

3 ———————

FIGURE 4

1 ———————

2 ———————

3 ———————

Beat the Bogey Babysitter

Horrid Henry hates babysitters – especially Rabid Rebecca, the toughest teen in town. He just wants to be left alone to watch TV and eat crisps all night. Could you beat the bogey babysitter or would you be sent to bed early? Take the quiz and find out.

1. Do you like having a babysitter?
(a) Yes, as long as it's somebody nice
(b) It's okay, but I miss Mum and Dad when they go out
(c) NO! I'm not a baby and I don't need to be sat on by a bossy teenager

2. What would your ideal babysitter be like?
(a) She'd play games with me and read me stories
(b) She'd help me if I asked her
(c) She'd let me stay up all night and eat sweets until I was sick

3. When Rabid Rebecca first arrives, how would you show her who's boss?
(a) I wouldn't, because she'd be in charge
(b) I'd sneak the biscuit tin up to my bedroom
(c) I'd hide her homework and 'accidentally' pour orange juice down the front of her new jeans

4. How would you annoy Rabid Rebecca when she's watching TV?
(a) Ask her politely if she'd mind changing channels
(b) Munch crisps very loudly in her ear
(c) Dance in front of the TV, blocking her view and singing as loudly as you can

. **What would you do if you didn't want Rabid Rebecca to babysit again?**

a) I'd stick my tongue out at her when she wasn't looking

b) I'd play loud music in my bedroom

c) I'd flood the bathroom

. **Do your babysitters return more than once?**

a) Yes, I always have the same lovely babysitter

b) Sometimes, but I've had a few different ones

c) No, my mum and dad say they can never go out, because they can't find a babysitter

ANSWERS

Mostly (a)s:
You're a babysitter's dream – well-behaved and polite, just like Perfect Peter. Someone as mean and moody as Rabid Rebecca would have you tucked up in bed without any supper, way before bedtime.

Mostly (b)s:
You might scare off a timid teenager, but not the snarling Rabid Rebecca. You'll need to be a lot noisier and naughtier to get rid of her.

Mostly (c)s:
Just like Horrid Henry, you know how to give Rabid Rebecca an evening she'll never forget – and she'll certainly never be back.

End of Term Party Tricks

It's time for the end of term party, and Magic Martha is entertaining the class with a couple of magic tricks. Why not try them on your family and friends too?

MIND READING

No one believes Magic Martha when she says she can read minds – until they see her do this trick!

MARTHA'S MAGIC TIP:
Don't let anyone see you writing the names or you'll give the game away

You will need:
- ★ Ten pieces of paper – all the same size
- ★ Pencil
- ★ Hat or bowl

Instructions:

1. Ask your audience to call out ten names from the Horrid Henry books.

2. Write down each name, then fold up the paper and put it in the hat. But – and this is the trick – don't really write down all the names. Only write down the first name called out – maybe it was BEEFY BERT – on all ten pieces of paper.

3. Ask a volunteer to come and pick out one of the pieces of paper from the hat. Tell them to read the name, but not to tell anyone what it is.

4. Now tell the audience that you are going to read your volunteer's mind. Ask your volunteer to concentrate very hard on the name, and look as though you're concentrating very hard too.

5. After a few seconds, announce to the audience that the name is BEEFY BERT!

JACK ATTACK

This is one of Magic Martha's favourite card tricks.

You will need:
- Pack of cards

Instructions:

1. Before you start, place one Jack at the top of the pack.

2. In front of your audience, search through the pack of cards for the other three Jacks. Leave the Jack you prepared earlier on the top and just show the other three to your audience.

3. Tell the audience that you are going to split up these three Jacks. Put one Jack on top of the pack, another Jack on the bottom and the last Jack somewhere in the middle.

4. Place the cards on the table and invite a volunteer to come and cut the pack. Now, the bottom section of cards will be at the top of the pack.

5. Ask your volunteer to look through the pack, and tell the audience to shout 'Jack Attack!'. Your volunteer will find three Jacks together in the same place.

MARTHA'S MAGIC TIP:
Show the Jacks to your audience very quickly, so they don't remember which suits they are.

Horrid Henry's Christmas Countdown

Thank you for my lovely advent calendar

You're the worst parents in the world!

Wednesday 1: Hooray! I can start opening my advent calendar. Aaaagh! There aren't any chocolates – just stupid boring pictures.

Thursday 2: I've started my letter to Father Christmas extra early – to make double sure he knows what I want. Remember, Father Christmas, satsumas are NOT presents.

Friday 3: Miss Battle-Axe has chosen the parts for the Christmas Nativity. Peter's Joseph and I'm the innkeeper, but I've only got one line. It's not fair! I should be the star of the show, not my stupid worm of a brother.

Saturday 4: Mum and Dad are so busy writing their Christmas cards, I get to watch TV all day. Tee hee!

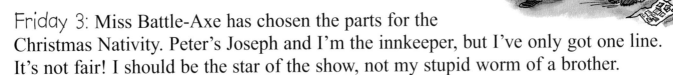

Sunday 5: Mum drags me out on a walk in the countryside to pick holly for decorations. This is the worst day of my life.

Monday 6: I've sneaked a bit of Mum's holly and put it on Miss Battle-Axe's chair. Tee hee!

Tuesday 7: We're making Christmas baubles at school. I'm going to throw mine at Peter on the way home!

Wednesday 8: We're rehearsing for the nativity. Miss Battle-Axe won't let me improve my part with a dance.

Thursday 9: I've found the secret Christmas Day sweet stash!

Friday 10: It's snowing!

Saturday 11: I bombed Peter with snowballs, but he cried, and Dad told me not to be horrid. Peter's a crybaby poopy pants!

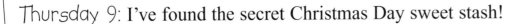

Sunday 12: Mum and Dad are baking horrible Christmassy food.

Monday 13: More rehearsals at school. Miss Battle-Axe won't let me add even a teeny-weeny-little song to my part.

Tuesday 14: I'm making the perfect present for Peter. A stinkbomb!

Wednesday 15: It's the school Christmas Fair – I've won a box of chocolates. Mum tells me I've got to give them to Granny.

Thursday 16: I've scoffed the chocolates. I won them – not Granny!

Friday 17: Mum and Dad are going Christmas shopping tomorrow, so I'm being extra nice to them. I even ate my vegetables at teatime.

Saturday 18: I had to trail around the shops with my family, and they didn't even buy me one tiny present. It's not fair! I ate loads of slimy vegetables for nothing.

Sunday 19: Peter is scratching out carols on his cello and Mum and Dad are singing. I'm playing the Smelly Bellies VERY loudly.

Monday 20: It's showtime! The nativity goes wrong – but I save the show. A star is born!

Tuesday 21: Last day of school. Hooray!

Wednesday 22: It's the holidays. I can watch TV for two weeks. Knight Fight – yeah!

Thursday 23: Oh no! I haven't got any presents for anybody. I write some nice Christmassy poems instead. Not bad, and cheap too!

Friday 24: I want Terminator Gladiator on the top of the Christmas tree. It looks much better than the stupid fairy that we always have.

Saturday 25: It's four o'clock on Christmas morning. I've opened all my presents and have chucked all my satsumas, socks and handkerchiefs in the bin where they belong. But Father Christmas wasn't completely useless this year – he got me a brilliant water pistol, so I'm having loads of fun spraying everyone. Mum and Dad don't look very pleased!

Henry's Hot Present Favourites

Here's Henry's Christmas present wish list, from his top hot favourites to his most hated gifts. Why don't you write your own list too?

HENRY'S LIST

A million pounds

Mega-gigantic TV with wraparound screen and 12 speakers

Megalatronic Animobotic Robots

Bugle Blast Boots

Mega-Whirl Goo-Shooter

Ballistic Bazooka Boomerangs

The Smelly Bellies Greatest Hits

Socks

Handkerchiefs

Lime green cardigan

Frilly pink lacy knickers

Baby Poopie Pants

HOT

COLD

YOUR LIST

_____

_____

_____

_____

_____

_____

_____

_____

_____

_____

_____

_____

_____

_____

My Christmas Lis

Dictionary
Stamps
Seeds
Geometry kit
Cello music

Thank you

by Perfect Peter

Follow the Footprints

"Frosty Freeze are having a best snowman competition," said Moody Margaret, glaring. "The winner gets a year's free supply of ice cream."

Read the full story in **Horrid Henry and the Abominable Snowman.**

Follow the footprints in the snow to find out who wins the ice cream. Is it Moody Margaret with her ballerina snowgirl, Horrid Henry with his Abominable Snowman or Perfect Peter with his bunny?

Saltdough Snowman

"You'll never win with that," jeered Horrid Henry. "Your snowman is pathetic."

"Better than yours," snapped Margaret.

Horrid Henry rolled his eyes.

"Obviously, because I haven't started on mine yet."

"We've got a big head start on you, so ha ha ha," said Susan. "We're building a ballerina snowgirl."

Discover who wins the competition in **Horrid Henry and the Abominable Snowman**.

SALTDOUGH SNOWMAN

Even if there's no snow, you can model your very own snowman – out of saltdough!

Instructions:

1. Mix the flour and salt in the mixing bowl, then stir in the water and oil.

2. Mix together with the fork.

3. If the mixture is dry and crumbly, add a bit more water. If it's too sticky, add more flour.

4. Sprinkle some flour on the table. Put your dough on the table, and knead it with your hands for about 10 minutes until it's smooth.

Now it's time to mould your snowman!

1. Mould the dough around a scrunched up ball of tin foil to form the body, then roll a smaller ball of dough for the head and attach to the body with a cocktail stick. You could also roll a carrot-shaped nose if you like.

2. Put the baking tray on a low shelf in the oven, and set the oven to its lowest temperature. Leave for around 3-4 hours.

3. When your snowman is hard, remove from the oven and leave to cool. Once cooled, use felt-tip pens, paint or anything else you can find to decorate!

You can make lots of other Christmassy things from saltdough – why not try a ballerina snowgirl like Moody Margaret's, or a bunny like Perfect Peter?

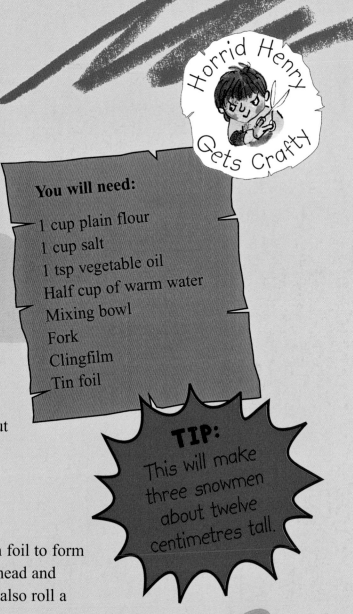

You will need:

1 cup plain flour
1 cup salt
1 tsp vegetable oil
Half cup of warm water
Mixing bowl
Fork
Clingfilm
Tin foil

TIP:
This will make three snowmen about twelve centimetres tall.

Horrid Henry Gets Crafty

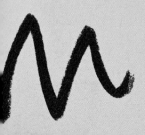

Brainy Brian's End of Year Quiz

So you think you know everything there is to know about Horrid Henry? Now it's time to find out the terrible truth with Brainy Brian's big quiz!

1. **When Horrid Henry gets all five spellings correct in the test, what is his reward from Miss Battle-Axe?**
   (a) A bag of Big Boppers
   (b) A gold star
   (c) Promotion to the top spelling group and twenty-five extra spellings to learn

2. **"Lumpy surprise with lumps. Gristly glop with globules." What is Horrid Henry describing?**
   (a) His mum's cooking
   (b) School dinners
   (c) The food at Perfect Peter's favourite restaurant, The Happy Carrot

3. **Where does Horrid Henry save his pocket money?**
   (a) In a skeleton bank
   (b) In a piggy bank
   (c) Under his pillow

4. **Horrid Henry is banned from trick or treating on Halloween because…**
   (a) His mum and dad don't want him to eat too many sweets
   (b) He cut off lots of Perfect Peter's hair
   (c) He's eaten all the satsumas his mum and dad bought for treats

5. **Where does Perfect Peter hide his diary?**
   (a) On his bookshelf, between *The Happy Nappy* and *The Hoppy Hippo*
   (b) In a pirate chest, buried in the garden
   (c) In his pants drawer

6. **When Dad asks Horrid Henry to name a vegetable he likes, what does Henry say?**
   (a) Cauliflower
   (b) Sprouts
   (c) Crisps

7. When they go shopping, why doesn't Henry want his mum to buy him a pair of pink and green trousers?

a) They're girls' trousers

b) They're too tight

c) They're too expensive

8. When his mum gives him a large cardboard box, what does Henry make out of it?

a) A sweet little house

b) A time machine

c) A den for the Purple Hand Club

9. There's only one vegetable that Perfect Peter doesn't like. Do you know what it is?

(a) Beetroot

(b) Sprouts

(c) Cabbage

10. What is Horrid Henry's favourite board game called?

(a) Winna

(b) Gotcha

(c) Betcha

How did you do? Turn to page 74 to find out.

7 – 10

You deserve to hold your head high. All that hard work reading lots of Horrid Henry books has definitely paid off. A year well spent!

4 – 6

Nothing to cheer about, but there's still hope. Pull up your socks, put in a few more reading hours, and you're sure to get a better score next year.

1 – 3

What have you been *doing* all year?

Horrid Henry's Christmas Play

"Isn't it exciting!" said Mum.

"Isn't it thrilling!" said Dad. "Our little boy, the star of the show."

"Well done, Peter," said Mum.

"We're so proud of you," said Dad.

Perfect Peter smiled modestly.

"Of course I'm not *really* the star," he said. "Everyone's important, even little parts like the blades of grass and the innkeeper."

Horrid Henry pounced. He was a Great White shark lunging for the kill.

"AAAARRRRGGGHH!" squealed Peter. "Henry bit me!"

"Henry! Don't be horrid!" snapped Mum.

"Henry! Go to your room!" snapped Dad.

Horrid Henry stomped upstairs and slammed the door. How could he bear the humiliation of playing the innkeeper when Peter was the star? He'd just have to force Peter to switch roles with him. Henry was sure he could find a way to persuade Peter, but persuading Miss Battle-Axe was a different matter. Miss Battle-Axe had a mean, horrible way of never doing what Henry wanted.

Maybe he could trick Peter into leaving the show. Yes! And then nobly offer to replace him.

But unfortunately, there was no guarantee Miss Battle-Axe would give Henry Peter's role.

She'd probably just replace Peter with Goody-Goody Gordon. He was stuck.

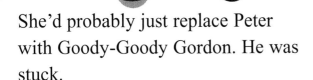

And then Horrid Henry had brilliant, spectacular idea. Why hadn't he thought of this before? If he couldn't play a bigger part, he'd just have to make his part bigger. For instance, he could scream "No." That would get a reaction. Or he could bellow "No," and then hit Joseph. I'm an angry innkeeper, thought Horrid Henry, and I hate guests coming to my inn. Certainly smelly ones like Joseph. Or he could shout "No!", hit Joseph, then rob him. I'm a robber innkeeper, thought Henry. Or, I'm a robber pretending to be an innkeeper. That would liven up the play a bit. Maybe he could be a French robber innkeeper, shout "Non", and rob Mary and Joseph. Or he was a French robber pirate innkeeper, so he could shout "Non," tie Mary and Joseph up and make them walk the plank. Hmmm, thought Horrid Henry. Maybe my part won't be so small. After all, the innkeeper was the most important character.

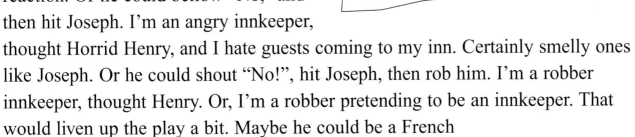

Find out what happens in **'Horrid Henry's Christmas Play'** from *Horrid Henry's Christmas Cracker*.

Horrid Henry's Christmas

Now, if only Mum and Dad would follow my advice, Christmas would be so much more fun!!!

Every single chocolate on the Christmas tree is to be eaten by me!!

I decide what to watch on TV.

Father Christmas must bring me EVERY single present I've asked for.

Anyone who gives me a lime green cardigan or a doll or socks or handkerchiefs or a dictionary is to be catapulted into outer space.

No sprouts or carrots or peas or ANY vegetables at Christmas lunch.

My horrible cousins Prissy Polly, Stuck-Up Steve, and Vomiting Vera must arrive, give me loads of presents, then leave immediately!

Christmas dinner must start with pudding.

HAPPY 2010 EVERYONE

Corny Christmas Cracker Jokes

Here are some of Horrid Henry's favourite Christmas cracker jokes:

What never eats at Christmas?
The turkey. It's usually stuffed.

What is Mum's favourite carol?
Silent night.

What do you get if you eat the Christmas decorations?
Tinselitis.

What goes red-white-red-white-red white?
Father Christmas rolling down a hill.

What do elves learn at elf school?
The elphabet.

Who says "oh oh oh"?
Father Christmas walking backwards.

What do snowmen eat for breakfast?
Snowflakes.

What do you get when you cross a vampire and a snowman?
Frost bite.

Mum, can I have a puppy for Christmas?
No, you can have turkey like everyone else.

What do monkeys sing at Christmas?
Jungle bells, jungle bells.

Puzzle Answers

There are **14** Filthy Fingerprints hidden in the Annual

Page 12 –
Horrid Henry vs Moody Margaret

	Henry	Margaret
1		✓
2		✓
3	✓	
4		✓
5	✓	
6	✓	

Page 20 –
Criss-Cross Conqueror

Page 22/23 –
Which Character is Which?

1. Moody Margaret
2. Horrid Henry
3. Perfect Peter
4. Sour Susan
5. Miss Battle-Axe

Page 26/27 –
Spot the Difference

1. Pencil – on the bedside table
2. Telescope – on top of the bookshelf
3. Xylophone – on the pillow
4. Drum – on the bed
5. Yo-yo – on the windowsill
6. Ball – on top of the dragon toy hanger
7. Piggy bank – in the purple box
8. Elephant – leaning against the wall
9. Book – on the floor, at the end of the bed
10. Nurse's bag – on the floor, in front of the bed

Page 30 –
Summer Holiday Wordsearch

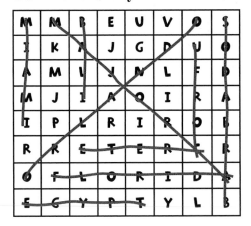

Page 32 – Little Brother and Sister-Taming tips

Horrid Henry would like to thank Barnaby Hudson, Daniel Roberts, Philip Cummings, Christopher Dixon and Lindsay and Isaac Hughes for their hilarious taming tips!

Page 37 –
Sandwich Criss-Cross

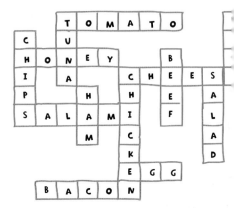

Page 40 –
Club Know-How Quiz

1. (c)
2. (b)
3. (b)
4. (a)
5. (c)
6. (b)
7. (a)
8. (b)

Page 42 –
Henry's Secret Code
STINKY FISH

Pages 43 –
Secret Club Code Circle
HENRY IS A BIG UGLY
TOADFACE

Page 44 –
Hello From Around the World

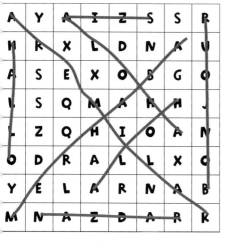

Page 45 –
Horrid Henry Goes to Play

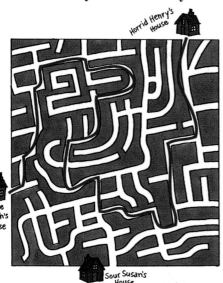

Page 47 –
Back to School Clock Puzzle
Henry dreams that his school has
been INVADED BY ALIENS

Page 51 –
Find the Halloween Pairs
The four matching pairs are:
A and D
B and G
C and E
F and H

Page 54 – Anxious Andrew's
Worried Wordsearch

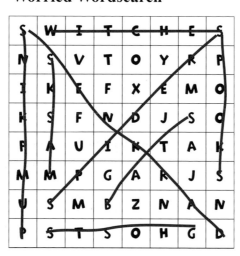

Page 55 –
Mad Misfits
FIGURE 1
1 – Miss Battle-Axe
2 – Perfect Peter
3 - Sour Susan
FIGURE 2
1 – Moody Margaret
2 – Greedy Graham
3 – Gorgeous Gurinder
FIGURE 3
1 – Henry's dad
2 – Sour Susan
3 – Brainy Brian
FIGURE 4
1 – Weepy William
2 – Soggy Sid
3 – Miss Battle-Axe

Page 63 –
Follow the Footprints
Perfect Peter and his bunny

Page 66 –
Brainy Brian's End of
Year Quiz
1. (c)
2. (b)
3. (a)
4. (b)
5. (a)
6. (c)
7. (a)
8. (b)
9. (a)
10. (b)

You can read these other *Horrid Henry* titles, stories available as audio editions, read by Miranda Richardson

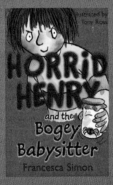

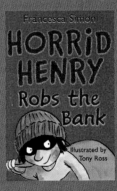

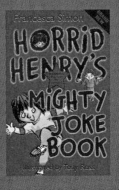

FRANCESCA SIMON

HORRID HENRY'S BIG BAD BOOK

Ten favourite stories – and more!

Illustrated by Tony Ross

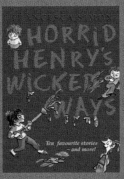

HORRID HENRY'S WICKED WAYS

Ten favourite stories – and more!

FRANCESCA SIMON

HORRID HENRY'S EVIL ENEMIES

Ten favourite stories – and more!

Illustrated by Tony Ross

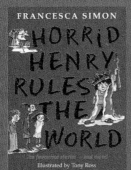

FRANCESCA SIMON

HORRID HENRY RULES THE WORLD

Ten favourite stories – and more!

Illustrated by Tony Ross

Francesca Simon

HORRID HENRY'S HOUSE OF HORRORS

Ten favourite stories – and more!

Illustrated by Tony Ross

Francesca Simon

HORRID HENRY'S DREADFUL DEEDS

Ten favourite stories – and more!

Illustrated by Tony Ross

HORRID HENRY'S Brainbusters

Activity book

HORRID HENRY'S Headscratchers

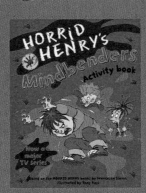

HORRID HENRY'S Mindbenders

Activity book

HORRID HENRY'S Colouring Book

HORRID HENRY'S Puzzle Book

HORRID HENRY'S Sticker Book

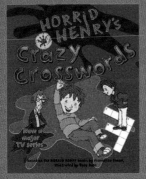

HORRID HENRY'S Crazy Crosswords

HORRID HENRY'S Mad Mazes

HORRID HENRY'S Wicked Wordsearches

HORRID HENRY'S Bumper fun

HORRID HENRY'S Classroom Chaos

HORRID HENRY'S Holiday Havoc

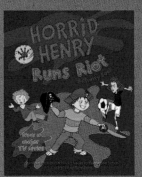

HORRID HENRY Runs Riot